Golfermania

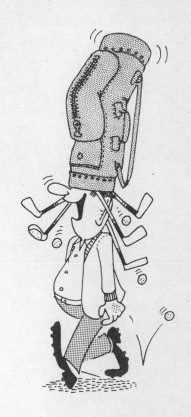

Cartoons by *Qvist*

Ravette Limited

British edition published by
Ravette Limited
© Ravette Ltd. 1985
Reprinted 1986

First published by
A/S Interpresse, Box 11, 2880 Bagsvaerd,
Copenhagen, Denmark.
© Hans Qvist of A/S Interpresse, 1983

Printed and bound in Great Britain
for Ravette Limited,
3 Glenside Estate,
Star Road, Partridge Green,
Horsham, Sussex RH13 8RA
by Cox & Wyman Ltd.,
Reading

ISBN 0 906710 69 3

Now, the 7th hole was the tricky one. Daddy's ball had landed right behind a tree, but I took my spoon and . . .

Was it on purpose you hit that little ball out in the lake, George?

That's the tricky part about golf, if your drive is
even just a tiny bit out . . .

Including the 4 children we had, it's been the best investment we ever made!

He insists on playing the ball from wherever it falls.

Sorry about the delay, boys. They just called from the clinic to tell me that my wife's given birth to a couple of something - or - other.

8

The picture became unsteady right in the middle
of next year's masters..

If I 'adn't been 'ere Guv'nor, you'd 'ave lost yer ball.
I grabbed it just as it was disappearin' down that 'ole.

Yes, John has taken up golf, but he can't quite
forget that he used to play billiards.

Well, you will just have to live with the fact, Mr Higgins,
that you'll probably never perfect your drive.

Will you never learn not to ask your father how his golf
went, when he comes home early?

But isn't there anything else you can do in winter, when golfing is out of season, Herbie?

Of course I can keep my head still and I'm going to prove it, dear!

And please send me a driver and a crate of balls.

How long have you been with the firm, Jones?

Can't you forget that slice of yours for even a moment, Edwin?

When for once you do the washing-up, darling,
I wish you'd do it with good grace.

We could do with more of his type. See how
he stuck to his club tie to the last.

18

What you seem to need, Mr Higgins, is some work to take your mind off your hobby.

Yes, I've seen 6 or 7 of those already. I wonder if they're part of some kind of drainage.

Shouldn't we forget about the ball, Sir, and try and find the course?

If you're goin' out golfing today, she said, it'll be over my dead body.

That's a new club record, guv'nor. Two and a 'alf twist.

Yes, yes, yes. But your ulcer will have to wait
until I've heard the results of the Open.

When you find the rule that says it's not permitted,
I'll take it off and not a moment before.

But if I give you these nice notes, couldn't
I just borrow it for an hour or two?

Golfers are the most stubborn people I've ever known.

24

Oh blast! Three inches out again.

Relax. This isn't going to take long . . .

Have I or haven't I stayed at home to help you
in the garden — yes or no?

Isn't it about time you faced facts?
That drive of yours is hardly perfect.

Hurry up, Bill. There's no queue up at the 1st tee at all.

Excuse me. Are all the bunkers on this course as bad as this one?

Wrong again, Edwin. That's not the lawn-mower.

Oh, stop snivelling. What's happened to my ball?

I said I'm sorry.

He's been like that ever since he missed that
6 inch putt the day before yesterday, doctor.

Is it today by any chance you're going
for a round of golf with the old boys?

34

No thanks — I'm driving.

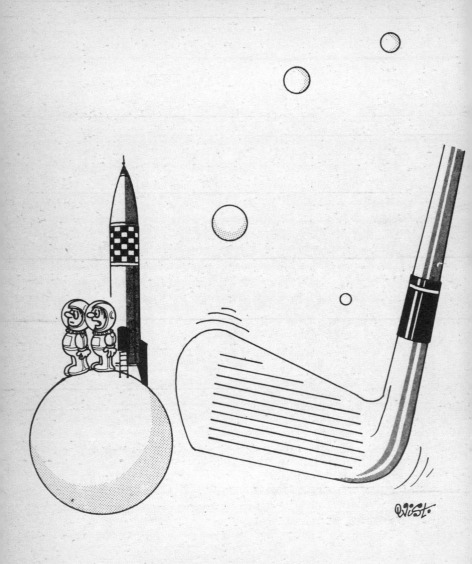

Well so far there's been no sign of life . . .

I've never been able to work out whether he's
overworked, plain lazy or out golfing.

Yes, quite. But what about your golf?

Experience tells me, we'd better get to bed.

This is certainly the toughest course I've yet seen.

And the best bit about this game is that there seems to be no parking problems.

Well, . . . at least the direction was right, dear.

And I'd advise you not to play more than 27 holes
a day for the next couple of weeks.

Oh those! They're just something Herbie has won at some game or other

Opener please.

Whoever he is, I don't fancy going a round with him.

His style may not be very elegant, but he's the hardest hitter in the club . . .

Golfing keeps him away from bars and night-clubs, but it was actually cheaper then.

What's new anyway old sport?

The nine iron please.

Are you trying to tell me you've had
a hole-in-one again, Herbert?

Well, sir – surely you know it's tough coming
back after a three weeks golfing holiday?

This, I think, has got to be the limit.

Remember the firm, steady grip, the rhythmic level stroke, and the smooth shoulder movement.

Sorry I'm late, boys. They added another psalm after the ceremony.

'Ere, guv'nor. Only 50 pence for my sensational
book: How To Be A Successful Golf-Pro.

I don't know what it is he's invented,
but he's never at home any more.

No, the General Manager went out about twenty minutes ago, but I'm expecting him back any minute!

Gee, Howard, it's ages since you put your arms around me like that

Now, my good man, will you please get up. You're lying on my ball.

HERBERT . . . !

Quite, sir. But then everybody needs a good laugh now and then.

You didn't think that a wedding would take all day, did you?

All I can say that I wouldn't care to go a round
with a fellow with that kind of temperament.

Too bad our marriage had to end this way, Cora.

I say, don't you ever relax from your work, Sir?

Really! There are times when I think you
go and get these chills on purpose.

On the other hand, Arnold says here
in the seventh chapter, paragraph fourteen . . .

Why, sure darling, you just pop into the club-house
and have a drink. It's your wedding, too.

We can't go on meeting like this, love.

Take a couple of aspirins, Mrs Jenkins and call me
again in a couple of hours if that hasn't helped.

Should that be taken as a hint that you want
more democracy in this office, Smith?

This happens every time I get a putter into my hands, doctor.

And you have a superb golf course right next door!

Your first hole-in-one, I presume?

Of course this is the happiest day in my life,
darling. I could never afford a caddie before.

And on what grounds have you applied for one day's liberty, Jones?

Well, he can't afford polo and he hasn't really got the time for golf.

He can never make up his mind which club to use.

They don't seem to be all that advanced. They just go around
hitting small, white balls with some strange kind of sticks . . .

And finally, when you've perfected your drive, you run out of balls.

It's all right for you bachelors, you have only yourselves to think of. But I'll be ready at the crack of dawn.

Well, she wasn't too keen on it, but at long last she said I could go.

Other cartoon books published by Ravette

Garfield Landscapes

Garfield The All-Round Sports Star	£1.95
Garfield The Irresistible	£1.95
Garfield On Vacation	£1.95
Garfield Weighs In	£1.95
Garfield I Hate Monday	£1.95
Garfield Special Delivery	£1.95
Garfield The Incurable Romantic	£1.95

Garfield paperbacks

No. 1 Garfield The Great Lover	£1.50
No. 2 Garfield Why Do You Hate Mondays?	£1.50
No. 3 Garfield Does Pooky Need You?	£1.50
No. 4 Garfield Admit It, Odie's OK!	£1.50
No. 5 Garfield Two's Company	£1.50
No. 6 Garfield What's Cooking?	£1.50
No. 7 Garfield Who's Talking?	£1.50
No. 8 Garfield Strikes Again	£1.50
No. 9 Garfield Here's Looking At You	£1.50
No. 11 Garfield Here We Go Again	£1.50
No. 10 Garfield We Love You Too	£1.50
No. 12 Garfield Life and Lasagne	£1.50

Introducing Snake	£2.50
Marmaduke Super dog	£2.50
Marmaduke 2	£2.50
Frank and Ernest	£1.95

All these books are available at your local bookshop or news-agent, or can be ordered direct from the publisher. Just tick the titles you require and fill in the form below. Prices and availability subject to change without notice.

Ravette Limited, 3 Glenside Estate, Star Road, Partridge Green, Horsham, West Sussex RH13 8RA

Please send a cheque or postal order, and allow the following for postage and packing. UK: Paperbacks – 45p for one book plus 20p for the second book and 15p for each additional book. Landscape Series – 45p for one book plus 30p for each additional book.

Name ....

Address ....

....